Kit

Unit 6 Reader

Skills Strand
KINDERGARTEN

Amplify learning.

Table of Contents

Kit

Unit 6 Reader

Kit

Kit can run.

Kit can skip.

Kit can flip and flop.

Kit can swim.

Kit and Stan

Kit ran and hid.

Stan ran and got Kit.

Stan ran and hid.

Kit ran and got Stan.

Kit and Stan had fun.

Kit's Hats

Kit ha**s** hats.

Kit ha**s** big hats.

Kit ha**s** flat hats.

Kit ha**s** fun hats.

Kit's Cats

Kit ha**s** cats.

Kit's cats run fast.

Kit's cats lap up milk.

Kit's cats jump up on Kit's bed.

KE

Kit's Mom

Kit's mom gets up at six.

Kit's mom gets dad up.

Kit's mom gets Kit up.

Kit's mom gets dad fed.

Kit's mom gets Kit fed.

Kit's mom gets Kit's pets fed.

Kit's Pants

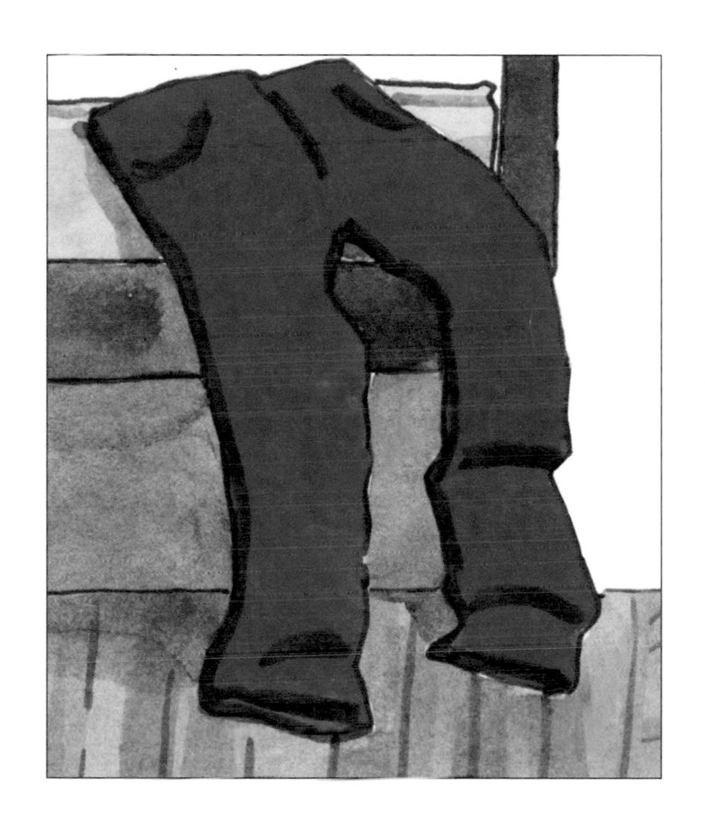

Kit had red pants.

Kit's pants got lost at camp.

Kit's mom got mad at Kit.

Kit's mom can't stand lost pants.

Mumps

Kit ha**s** mumps.

Kit i**s** in bed.

Kit can't get up.

Kit can't run and jump.

Kit can't skip and hop.

Kit **is** sad.

Up

Kit gets up on top.

Kit helps Max get up.

Max helps Jen get up.

Jen helps Kent get up.

Kent helps Ted get up.

Ted helps Peg get up.

Fast Fred

Kit's pal Fred gulps his milk.

Fast Fred gulps and gulps.

Fred gets milk on his desk.

Fred gets milk on his pants.

Fred gets milk on Kit.

Kit gets mad at Fred.

“Stop it, Fred!”

Pip's Cats

Pip i**s** Kit's pal.

Pip ha**s** six cats.

Pip's cats got in mud.

Pip's cats left mud on hi**s** rug.

Pip's mom got mad.

Vic Gets Lost

Pip's cat Vic got lost.

Pip felt sad.

Kit ran and got Vic.

Kit set Vic on Pip's lap.

Pip felt glad.

About this Book

This book has been created for use by students learning to read with the Core Knowledge Reading Program. Readability levels are suitable for early readers. The book has also been carefully leveled in terms of its "code load," or the number of spellings used in the stories.

The English writing system is complex. It uses more than 200 spellings to stand for 40-odd sounds. Many sounds can be spelled several different ways, and many spellings can be pronounced several different ways. This book has been designed to make early reading experiences simpler and more productive by using a subset of the available spellings. It uses *only* spellings students have been taught to sound out as part of their phonics lessons, plus a handful of tricky words, which have also been deliberately introduced in the lessons. This means the stories will be 100% decodable if they are assigned at the proper time.

As the students move through the program, they learn new spellings and the "code load" in the decodable readers increases gradually. The code load graphic on this page indicates the number of spellings students are expected to know in order to read the first story of the book and the number of spellings students are expected to know in order to read the final stories in the book. The columns on the opposite page list the specific spellings and Tricky Words students are expected to recognize at the beginning of this reader. The bullets at the bottom of the opposite page identify spellings, tricky words, and other topics that are introduced gradually in the unit this reader accompanies.

Visit us on the web at www.coreknowledge.org

Core Knowledge Language Arts

Series Editor-in-Chief
E. D. Hirsch, Jr.

President
Linda Bevilacqua

Editorial Staff
Carolyn Gosse, Senior Editor - Preschool
Khara Turnbull, Materials Development Manager
Michelle L. Warner, Senior Editor - Listening & Learning

Mick Anderson
Robin Blackshire
Maggie Buchanan
Paula Coyner
Sue Fulton
Sara Hunt
Erin Kist
Robin Luecke
Rosie McCormick
Cynthia Peng
Liz Pettit
Ellen Sadler
Deborah Samley
Diane Auger Smith
Sarah Zelinke

Design and Graphics Staff
Scott Ritchie, Creative Director

Kim Berrall
Michael Donegan
Liza Greene
Matt Leech
Bridget Moriarty
Lauren Pack

Consulting Project Management Services
ScribeConcepts.com

Additional Consulting Services
Ang Blanchette
Dorrit Green
Carolyn Pinkerton

Acknowledgments

These materials are the result of the work, advice, and encouragement of numerous individuals over many years. Some of those singled out here already know the depth of our gratitude; others may be surprised to find themselves thanked publicly for help they gave quietly and generously for the sake of the enterprise alone. To helpers named and unnamed we are deeply grateful.

Contributors to Earlier Versions of these Materials

Susan B. Albaugh, Kazuko Ashizawa, Nancy Braier, Kathryn M. Cummings, Michelle De Groot, Diana Espinal, Mary E. Forbes, Michael L. Ford, Ted Hirsch, Danielle Knecht, James K. Lee, Diane Henry Leipzig, Martha G. Mack, Liana Mahoney, Isabel McLean, Steve Morrison, Juliane K. Munson, Elizabeth B. Rasmussen, Laura Tortorelli, Rachael L. Shaw, Sivan B. Sherman, Miriam E. Vidaver, Catherine S. Whittington, Jeannette A. Williams

We would like to extend special recognition to Program Directors Matthew Davis and Souzanne Wright who were instrumental to the early development of this program.

Schools

We are truly grateful to the teachers, students, and administrators of the following schools for their willingness to field test these materials and for their invaluable advice: Capitol View Elementary, Challenge Foundation Academy (IN), Community Academy Public Charter School, Lake Lure Classical Academy, Lepanto Elementary School, New Holland Core Knowledge Academy, Paramount School of Excellence, Pioneer Challenge Foundation Academy, New York City PS 26R (The Carteret School), PS 30X (Wilton School), PS 50X (Clara Barton School), PS 96Q, PS 102X (Joseph O. Loretan), PS 104Q (The Bays Water), PS 214K (Michael Friedsam), PS 223Q (Lyndon B. Johnson School), PS 308K (Clara Cardwell), PS 333Q (Goldie Maple Academy), Sequoyah Elementary School, South Shore Charter Public School, Spartanburg Charter School, Steed Elementary School, Thomas Jefferson Classical Academy, Three Oaks Elementary, West Manor Elementary.

And a special thanks to the CKLA Pilot Coordinators Anita Henderson, Yasmin Lugo-Hernandez, and Susan Smith, whose suggestions and day-to-day support to teachers using these materials in their classrooms was critical.

Credits

Every effort has been taken to trace and acknowledge copyrights. The editors tender their apologies for any accidental infringement where copyright has proved untraceable. They would be pleased to insert the appropriate acknowledgment in any subsequent edition of this publication. Trademarks and trade names are shown in this publication for illustrative purposes only and are the property of their respective owners. The references to trademarks and trade names given herein do not affect their validity.

All photographs are used under license from Shutterstock, Inc. unless otherwise noted.

Writers

Matt Davis, Juliane K. Munson

Illustrators and Image sources

All illustrations by Kristin Kwan